Oh No, Hippo!

by **Heather Pindar**
illustrated by **Angelika Scudamore**

"It's my birthday," said Chimp.

"Let's swing from tree to tree."

Chimp swung.

Flamingo and Zebra swung too.

But not...

...Hippo.

SWISH! BANG! He hit the tree.

SPLAT! Hippo fell into Chimp's birthday cake.

"Oh no, Hippo!" said everyone.

"It's my birthday," said Zebra.

"Let's run as fast as we can."

Chimp and Flamingo ran after Zebra.

But not...

TRIP! THUMP!

Hippo fell into Zebra's birthday cake.

"Oh no, Hippo!" said everyone.

"It's my birthday," said Flamingo.

"Everyone hop like me."

18

Hop, hop, hop went Flamingo,
Chimp and Zebra.

But not...

...Hippo.

SPIN! CRASH!

SPLAT! Hippo fell into Flamingo's birthday cake.

"Oh no, Hippo!" said everyone.

One hot afternoon Hippo said,
"Let's go for a swim."

Hippo swam.

But not Chimp, Zebra and Flamingo.

"Hop on my back," said Hippo.

"What fun!" said Zebra.

"This is the best!" said Flamingo.

"I see cakes," said Chimp.

"1... 2... 3... cakes!"

"Do you like the cakes?" said Hippo.

"Oh YES!" said everyone.

"Thank you, Hippo!"

Quiz

1. What did Monkey do for his birthday?
a) Run
b) Swing
c) Hop

2. What happened to the cakes?
a) Hippo fell into them
b) The animals ate them
c) They were stolen

3. What did Hippo trip on?
a) A branch
b) A rock
c) A tree

4. Who likes swimming?
a) Flamingo
b) Zebra
c) Hippo

5. What did Hippo give at the end?
a) Party bags
b) Balloons
c) New cakes

Turn over for answers

Book Bands for Guided Reading

Pink
Red
Yellow
Blue
Green
Orange
Turquoise
Purple
Gold
White

The Institute of Education book banding system is a scale of colours that reflects the various levels of reading difficulty. The bands are assigned by taking into account the content, the language style, the layout and phonics. Word, phrase and sentence level work is also taken into consideration.

Maverick Early Readers are a bright, attractive range of books covering the pink to white bands. All of these books have been book banded for guided reading to the industry standard and edited by a leading educational consultant.

To view the whole Maverick Readers scheme, visit our website at

www.maverickearlyreaders.com

Or scan the QR code above to view our scheme instantly!

Quiz Answers: 1b, 2a, 3b, 4c, 5c